Learning & Caring About OUR WORLD

By Gayle Bittinger

Illustrated by Kathy Jones

Warren Publishing House, Inc.
Everett, Washington

This book is dedicated to the special people who taught me, through their words and actions, how to love and care for our world – my parents and my husband.

G.B.

Some of the activity ideas in this book were originally contributed by *Totline Newsletter* subscribers. We wish to acknowledge Marjorie Debowey, Stony Brook, NY; Marion Ekberg, Gig Harbor, WA; Ellen Javernick, Loveland, CO; Neoma Kreuter, Ontario, CA; Rose C. Merenda, Warwick, RI; Lois Olson, Webster City, IA; Susan M. Paprocki, Northbrook, IL; Susan Peters, Upland, CA; Colraine Pettipaw Hunley, Doylestown, PA; Betty Silkunas, Lansdale, PA; Inez Stewart, West Baraboo, WI; Kristine Wagoner, Federal Way, WA; Betty June Loew White, Amarillo, TX; Nancy Windes, Denver, CO.

Editorial Staff: Elizabeth McKinnon, Susan M. Sexton, Jean Warren

Production Staff: Eileen Carbary, Kathy Jones, Kerrie Carbary

Design: Kathy Jones

ISBN 0-911019-30-8

Library of Congress Catalog Card Number 89-052145
Printed in the United States of America
Published by: Warren Publishing House, Inc.
        P.O. Box 2250
        Everett, WA 98203

Introduction

Taking care of the environment is an important but sometimes overwhelming job for adults. The job seems even more overwhelming when you want to teach young children about the environment. Where do you start?

As I sat down to write this book, I had to answer that question for myself. I decided that the following three areas were the best places to begin:

- Teach young children about the environment – land, air and water – at their level and help them develop an appreciation for the world they live in through activities that include hands-on science, art, music, movement and learning games,

- Provide young children with opportunities to contribute to the care and well-being of their world,

- Give parents and children activities to do together to learn about and take care of their environment.

With these starting places in mind, I put together the material you will find in this book: developmentally appropriate activities that help young children explore, understand and appreciate the world around them; ideas for easy but important things that young children can do to help take care of their world; and reproducible parent flyers that are filled with ideas for children and parents to do together.

It is my hope that you will find the activities in this book to be fun and easy ways to encourage your children to learn and take care of Our World.

Contents

OUR LAND

How We Get Dirt

Materials: Several rocks (granite or sandstone, if possible); a box of sand; a box of dirt.

Preparation: None.

Activity: Explain to the children that dirt, or soil, is made from rocks, plants and animals. First, show them the rocks and the sand. Tell them that after years and years of warming by the sun, freezing by the snow and ice and wearing away by the wind and rain, the rock will eventually break into smaller and smaller pieces until it becomes sand. Then show the children the dirt. Explain that dirt is sand with tiny pieces of decaying plants and animals in it. Let the children take turns feeling the sand and the dirt. How does the dirt feel different from the sand? Does the dirt look different?

Dirt Safari

Materials: Newspaper; spade or shovel; sifters; magnifying glasses.

Preparation: None.

Activity: Go outside with the children. Spread newspaper on a level surface and put two or three scoops of dirt on it. Give the children sifters and magnifying glasses to use to examine the dirt. Can they see any parts of plants, animals or rocks in the dirt? What does the dirt feel and smell like?

I Love Dirt

Sung to: "Three Blind Mice"

I love dirt, I love dirt.
Fun, brown dirt; fun, brown dirt.
I love to dig down in the ground,
I love to have dirt all around,
I love to pile it in a mound.
I love dirt.

Gayle Bittinger

Making Dirt

Materials: Cut-up fruit and vegetable skins; sand; peat moss; eggshells; bean seeds; pitcher of water; paper cups; spoons.

Preparation: Set out the materials.

Activity: Let the children help you tear fruit and vegetable skins into small pieces and crush eggshells into tiny bits. Then give them paper cups and spoons. Have each child put in his or her cup a spoonful of sand, a spoonful of peat moss, a few pieces of fruit and vegetable skins and some crushed eggshell. Let the children add small amounts of water to their cups before stirring all their ingredients together. They now have dirt. Give each of the children one or two bean seeds to plant in their cups. Have them set their cups in the sun and add water regularly. Why are their seeds growing? What is in dirt that seeds need to grow?

Variation: If desired, let the children make their own sand by wrapping small sandstone rocks in a towel and crushing them with a hammer.

Mud Sculpting

Materials: Bucket of dirt; kitchen basters; dishpans; bowl of water.

Preparation: Set out the materials.

Activity: Let the children use their hands to put scoops of dirt in the dishpans. Have them use the kitchen basters to add water to the dirt to make mud. Let them play and be creative with the mud in their dishpans. What would happen if they added more dirt? What would happen if they added more water? Ask them to describe how the mud feels. Does it feel cold? Warm? Squishy? Slimy? Smooth? Rough?

Mud Song

Sung to: "Skip to My Lou"

Scoop up some dirt and add a little water,
Scoop up some dirt and add a little water,
Scoop up some dirt and add a little water.
That's how I make mud.

Squish it with my hands and pat it in a pie,
Squish it with my hands and pat it in a pie,
Squish it with my hands and pat it in a pie.
That's what I do with mud.

Gayle Bittinger

Earthworm Observation

Materials: Mirror; glass pie plate; earthworm.

Preparation: Place a mirror on a table with a glass pie plate upside down over it. Put an earthworm on top of the pie plate.

Activity: Let the children observe the earthworm as seen from above and as reflected in the mirror. Ask them such questions as "How does the earthworm move? What color is it? What does its skin look like?" Talk about what earthworms do in the soil. Explain that they hatch from eggs that are inside a cocoon. The worms are very tiny when they are born and many worms hatch from one cocoon. The worms dig tunnels in the dirt to live in. The only facial feature an earthworm has is a mouth through which soil (an earthworm's food) enters. Little piles of an earthworm's digested soil can be found near the opening of its tunnel. These piles are called castings.

Earthworm Hunt

Materials: Spade or shovel; plastic container.

Preparation: Find a spot where there are many earthworms, such as a garden or a compost pile. Or "seed" a small area with worms you have found in other places. (If necessary, check with a sporting goods store to find out where earthworms can be purchased in your area.)

Activity: Take the children on a nature walk to your pre-selected site. Talk about the kinds of places earthworms like to live in, such as gardens or other spots with dark brown soil. When you reach your site, use a spade or shovel to turn over the soil and let the children look for worms. Put the worms in a plastic container with enough damp soil to cover them. Then take the worms back to observe.

Extension: When your observation of earthworms is finished, let the children help return the worms to a garden or other appropriate place.

Earthworm

Sung to: "Did You Ever See a Lassie?"

Did you ever see an earthworm,
An earthworm, an earthworm,
Did you ever see an earthworm
Move this way and that?
Move this way and that way,
Move this way and that way.
Did you ever see an earthworm
Move this way and that?

Have the children move their fingers,
arms or bodies like earthworms as they
sing the song.

Betty Silkunas

Worm Tracks

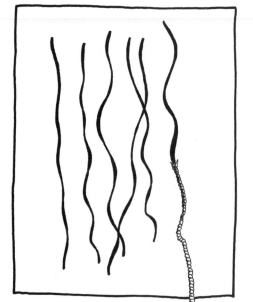

Materials: Shallow containers; brown termpera paint; string; construction paper; pair of scissors.

Preparation: Pour small amounts of brown tempera paint into shallow containers. Cut string into 6-inch pieces.

Activity: Give each child a piece of construction paper and a 6-inch piece of string. Let the children dip their pieces of string in the brown tempera paint. Then have them pull their strings across their papers to make "worm tracks." Encourage them to make their strings crawl and wiggle like real worms.

Plants Need Water

Materials: Two identical houseplants that need frequent watering; such as a coleus, a peace lily or an umbrella plant; watering can; water.

Preparation: Place two identical houseplants that need frequent watering in a window. Fill a watering can with water.

Activity: Let the children take turns watering just one of the plants. After several days have them compare the plants. Which plant looks healthy? Which plant looks droopy? Can they name one thing that plants need to grow? Now let the children water both of the plants until they both look healthy again.

Hydroponic Gardening

Materials: Short wide-mouthed clear plastic cups; tall narrow-mouthed clear plastic cups; vermiculite (available at garden supply stores); bean or lettuce seeds; liquid plant food; sponge; watering can; water; pair of scissors.

Preparation: Poke holes in the bottoms of short wide-mouthed plastic cups, one hole in each. Put a 1/4- by 3-inch strip of sponge through the hole of each cup. Mix water and liquid plant food in a watering can according to the directions on the plant food bottle.

Activity: Explain to the children that plants can grow without soil. This kind of gardening is called hydroponic gardening. Give each child one of the short wide-mouthed cups with a sponge strip in it and a tall narrow-mouthed cup. Let the children fill their tall cups partway with water from the watering can. Have them carefully place their short cups on top of their tall cups so that the sponge strips hang down into the water. Let them fill their short cups with vermiculite. Give them each several bean or lettuce seeds to plant in the vermiculite. Set the cups in a sunny location. Have the children observe their cups over the next week as their seeds begin to sprout. How can their plants grow without soil? (Soil provides plants with two things: support and nutrients. Hydroponic gardens provide support with vermiculite and nutrients with liquid plant food.) Have the children add the water and fertilizer mixture to their tall cups as necessary.

Caution: Children need adult supervision at all times while working with fertilizer.

Plants Need Light

Materials: Two identical house-plants that grow best in a sunny place, such as a corn plant, a rubber tree or ivy; watering can; water.

Preparation: Set out two identical houseplants that grow best in a sunny location. Fill a watering can with water.

Activity: Have the children help you place one of the plants by a sunny window and the other plant in a dark place such as a closet or a cabinet. Let the children take turns watering both plants. After a while set the two plants out on a table. Ask the children to describe the differences in the plants. Why does one of the plants look unhealthy? What could they do to make it look healthy again? What is something plants need to grow?

What Do Plants Need?

Sung to: "The Mulberry Bush"

Little plant, oh, what do you need,
What do you need, what do you need?
Little plant, oh, what do you need,
To grow up big and strong?

I need water to stand up tall,
Stand up tall, stand up tall.
I need water to stand up tall,
To grow up big and strong.

I need sun to make my food,
Make my food, make my food.
I need sun to make my food,
To grow up big and strong.

I need support for roots and stems,
Roots and stems, roots and stems.
I need support for roots and stems,
To grow up big and strong.

I need nutrients to keep me healthy,
Keep me healthy, keep me healthy.
I need nutrients to keep me healthy,
To grow up big and strong.

Jean Warren

Seed Transporting

Materials: A pair of old white socks for each child.

Preparation: None.

Activity: Help the children each put on a pair of old white socks over their shoes. Then take the children on a seed-collecting hike. If possible, hike through a park or the woods. As you walk along, have the children look at their socks every now and then. Do they see any seeds on them? Where did the seeds come from? What will happen when they shake the seeds off their socks when they get back? Explain to them that this is one way that seeds get moved, or transported, to new areas where they fall to the ground, get covered with dirt and begin to grow. Could animals transport seeds? How?

Extension: Have the children carefully shake some of their seeds into a tray of dirt. Place the tray in a sunny place and add water regularly. Let the children observe any seeds that sprout.

When Animals Walk Around

Sung to: "My Bonnie Lies Over the Ocean"

When animals walk around,
Past flowers and grass and trees,
The animals' fur and feet
Pick up the plants' seeds.
Seeds, seeds, seeds, seeds,
Their fur picks up the seeds, the
    seeds.
Seeds, seeds, seeds, seeds,
Their fur picks up the seeds.

Now later the seeds fall off,
And drop right down to the ground.
That's one way seeds for flowers
And grass and trees get 'round.
Seeds, seeds, seeds, seeds,
That's one way they get around,
    around.
Seeds, seeds, seeds, seeds,
That's one way they get around.

Jean Warren

Sprouting Seeds

Materials: Recloseable plastic sandwich bags; popcorn kernels; small kitchen baster; pan of dirt; bowl of water; spoon.

Preparation: Set out a pan of dirt with a spoon in it, a bowl of water, popcorn kernels and a small kitchen baster.

Activity: Give each child a recloseable plastic sandwich bag and have him or her put a spoonful of dirt in it. Then let the children each add two or three popcorn kernels to the dirt. Have them add water to their bags with the kitchen baster. Help the children seal their bags. Then hang the bags in a sunny window. The popcorn kernels will begin to sprout in about a week.

Planters

Materials: Tin cans; can opener; small rocks or gravel; dirt; flower seeds; watering can; water; various decorating materials such as yarn, fabric scraps, self-stick paper, construction paper, crayons; glue; masking tape.

Preparation: Use a can opener to completely remove one end completely from each of several tin cans. Check the rims of the cans for rough edges and cover them with masking tape if necessary. Set out the cans, glue and the decorating materials. Fill a watering can with water.

Activity: Let the children use the decorating materials to decorate their cans any way they wish. When they have finished, have them each

put a layer of small rocks or gravel in the bottoms of their cans. Then let them add dirt. Give each child several flower seeds to plant in his or her planter. Set the planters by a sunny window. Have the children use the watering can to water their seeds as needed. Encourage them to check regularly for signs of growth.

Vegetable Snacking

Materials: A variety of vegetables; peeler; knife; serving tray; plates; one or two vegetable dips (see recipes below).

Preparation: Prepare a variety of vegetables for snacking, setting aside a whole vegetable of each kind. Place the vegetables on a serving tray. Set out vegetable dip.

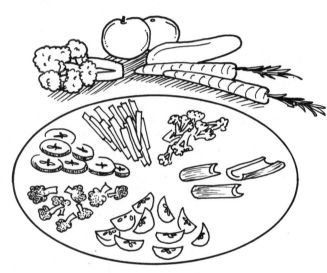

Activity: Have the children sit down at a table. Show them the prepared vegetables. Hold up the whole vegetables, one at a time, and ask the children to point to the matching prepared vegetables. Then give the children plates and let them choose the vegetables they would like to try. Put a spoonful of dip on each child's plate. Have the children tell you which vegetables they like best.

Cottage Cheese Dip — Combine ranch dressing mix with cottage cheese to taste. Stir well. If desired, place in a blender container with a small amount of milk and process until smooth.

Mustard Dip — Combine equal parts of plain yogurt and mayonnaise. Add mustard to taste.

Yogurt Dip — Combine yogurt, lemon juice and Italian dressing mix to taste.

Vegetables Are Plants We Eat

Sung to: "Mary Had a Little Lamb"

Vegetables are plants we eat,
They're so good, what a treat.
Carrots, beans and broccoli,
They help us grow so healthily.

Gayle Bittinger

Parts of a Plant

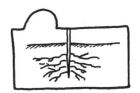

Materials: Clear plastic cup; bean seeds; dirt; water; index card or posterboard; felt-tip markers; pair of scissors.

Preparation: About a week before doing this activity, fill a clear plastic cup with dirt and plant a few bean seeds in it, close to one side. Water the seeds as necessary. On an index card or piece of posterboard, use felt-tip markers to draw a picture of a bean plant with its roots, stem and leaves. Cut the picture in three puzzle pieces, each one with a different plant part on it.

Activity: Show the children one of the bean plants growing in the cup.

Help them name the different parts of the plant, including the roots, which should be visible through the side of the cup. Then set out the puzzle pieces and let the children take turns putting the puzzle together and identifying the different plant parts.

Hint: If the roots of the plant do not show through the side of the cup, gently remove the plant for the demonstration and replant it later.

My Garden

This is my garden, I've raked it with care,
And planted my tiny brown flower seeds there.
I patted the earth, smoothed over the bed,
While the warm yellow sun shone high overhead.
Soon raindrops came pattering over the ground,
And warm spring winds blew with a soft gentle sound.
The little seeds woke and pushed up toward the light,
Up, up they grew slowly by day and by night.
And now see my garden, so lovely and gay,
With all of the flowers that blossomed today.

Author Unknown

Additional verse: Repeat the poem, substituting the words "vegetable seeds" for "flower seeds" in line two and changing the last line to read: "With all the ripe vegetables growing today."

The Trees Are Growing

Sung to: "The Farmer in the Dell"

The trees are growing tall,
>   (Raise arms above head, fingers touching.)
The trees are growing tall.
With soil and rain and sunny days,
The trees are growing tall.

The trees are growing roots,
>   (Bend over and touch floor.)
The trees are growing roots.
With soil and rain and sunny days,
The trees are growing roots.

The trees are growing bark,
>   (Run hands up and down sides.)
The trees are growing bark.
With soil and rain and sunny days,
The trees are growing bark.

The trees are growing branches,
>   (Stretch arms out.)
The trees are growing branches.
With soil and rain and sunny days,
The trees are growing branches.

The trees are growing leaves,
>   (Wiggle fingers.)
The trees are growing leaves.
With soil and rain and sunny days,
The trees are growing leaves.

Susan Peters

Adopt-A-Tree

Materials: As needed (see below).

Preparation: None.

Activity: Have the children choose a nearby tree to adopt. Visit the tree regularly and try to incorporate it into activities throughout the year, such as the following:

• Play circle games, such as Ring Around the Rosie or Duck, Duck, Goose, around the tree.

• Make leaf and bark rubbings.

• Pick up litter around the tree.

• Talk into a tape recorder and describe what the tree looks like in a particular season.

• Observe the animals that live in or near the tree.

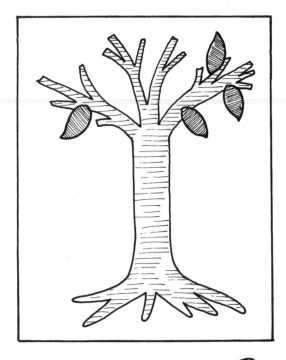

Parts of a Tree

Materials: Brown and green felt; various colors of felt scraps; flannelboard; pair of scissors.

Preparation: Cut out a brown felt tree shape that includes roots, a tree trunk and branches. Cut leaf shapes out of green felt. Cut several different kinds of fruit and nut shapes, such as apples, oranges, walnuts and almonds out of felt scraps.

Activity: Place the tree shape on a flannelboard. Point out the different parts of the tree. Then show the children the felt shapes. Talk about the different kinds of fruits and nuts that grow on trees. Then let the children take turns putting the leaf, fruit and nut shapes on the felt tree.

Made From Trees

Materials: Objects that are made from wood; objects that are not made from wood.

Preparation: Set out objects that are made from wood, such as a newspaper, a book, a toothpick, a pencil and a block. Set out other objects that are not made from wood, such as a plastic toy car, a cotton towel, a crayon, a metal spoon and a mirror.

Activity: Explain to the children that many of the objects we use every day are made from trees. Show them the objects you collected. Let them help you sort the items into two piles. Ask them if they can think of other things that are made from trees.

Extension: Have the children go on a tree hunt around the room to search for other objects that are made from trees.

Tree Snacks

Materials: Foods that grow on trees (see below); plates.

Preparation: Prepare for eating, foods that grow on trees, such as fruits (apples, oranges, bananas and pears), nuts (walnuts, almonds and pecans), olives, and chocolate (which is made from the seeds of the cacao tree). Arrange the foods on plates.

Activity: Show the children the different foods that come from trees. Ask them to name each one. Give each of the children a plate. Let them each choose several different "tree snacks" to put on their plates that they would like to taste.

Plant-A-Forest

Materials: Rectangular cake pan; brown playdough; nature magazines; tongue depressors; glue; pair of scissors.

Preparation: Cut pictures of things you would find in a forest, such as trees, plants, berry bushes, squirrels, birds, raccoons and bears out of nature magazines. Glue each picture to a tongue depressor. Fill a rectangular cake pan part way with brown playdough. Set out the pan and the tongue depressors.

Activity: Let the children take turns planting their own forests by sticking the ends of the tongue depressors into the playdough. Encourage them to name each item as they plant it.

Forest Animal Homes

Materials: Three boxes; nature magazines; felt-tip markers; pair of scissors.

Preparation: Collect three boxes. Use felt-tip markers to draw a picture of a cave on one box, a picture of a burrow on another box and a picture of a tree on a third box. Cut pictures of forest animals out of nature magazines.

Activity: Explain to the children that forest animals live in several different kinds of homes. Some animals live in dens or caves, some live in burrows in the ground and some live in trees. Set out the animal home boxes. Give the children pictures of the forest animals. Have each child name the animal in his or her picture, tell where it would most like to live and put the picture in the corresponding box.

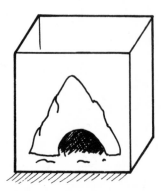

Animal Signs

Materials: None.

Preparation: Plan a walk through an area where you would be likely to find signs of animals, such as tracks, feathers, fur, nests and burrows. Take the walk by yourself beforehand and make notes of places where you find animal signs.

Activity: Take the children on your planned walk. Stop at the places where you found signs of animals and ask the children to look around carefully. Can they see any animal signs? Ask them to look for animal tracks, fur, feathers, nests and burrows. When they find a sign, ask them if they can guess which animal left it.

Extension: Let the children use magnifying glasses to examine the animal signs they find.

Through the Forest

Materials: None.

Preparation: None.

Activity: Have the children pretend to be different forest animals. Encourage them to fly like birds, scamper like chipmunks, leap gracefully like deer, lumber along like bears and be sly like foxes.

In the Forest You Will Find

Sung to: "If You're Happy and You Know It"

In the forest you will find great big trees,
In the forest you will find great big trees,
Growing oh, so very tall,
It's so hard to see them all.
In the forest you will find great big trees.

In the forest you will find bushy plants,
In the forest you will find bushy plants,
Growing red and growing green,
There are so many to be seen.
In the forest you will find bushy plants.

In the forest you will find bright berries,
In the forest you will find bright berries.
The birds do love them so,
'Cause the berries help them grow.
In the forest you will find bright berries.

In the forest you will find raccoons and squirrels,
In the forest you will find raccoons and squirrels.
Scampering here and all around,
Picking nuts up off the ground.
In the forest you will find raccoons and squirrels.

In the forest you will find bears and deer,
In the forest you will find bears and deer.
With their babies close at hand,
They love to roam across the land.
In the forest you will find bears and deer.

Gayle Bittinger

Gathering Up Nuts

Materials: Nuts; four baskets.

Preparation: Put nuts in two baskets.

Activity: Tell the children that many animals, such as squirrels and chipmunks, gather nuts to eat during the cold winter when food is hard to find. Then divide the children into two groups and have the groups stand at one end of the room. Give each group an empty basket. Place the two baskets filled with nuts at the other end of the room. Have the child in the front of each line scamper on all fours (like a squirrel) to a basket filled with nuts, take one of the nuts out with his or her hand and bring it back to his or her group's basket before the next child scampers off. Continue until each child has had a turn bringing back one of the nuts. Together, count the nuts in each group's basket.

Observing Birds

Materials: Plastic soft drink bottle; birdseed; 7-inch piece of 1/4-inch wooden dowel; twine; nail; craft knife; hole punch.

Preparation: Use a craft knife to cut two 2- to 3-inch holes directly across from each other in a plastic soft drink bottle. Use a hole punch to make a small hole 1 inch below each larger hole. Insert a 7-inch piece of 1/4-inch wooden dowel through the two small holes. Use a nail to poke two holes across from each other near the top of the bottle. Thread a piece of twine through the holes to make a hanger.

Activity: Let the children help you fill the bird feeder with birdseed. Hang the feeder outside in a place that the children can see from a window. Have the children watch for birds to come visit the feeder.

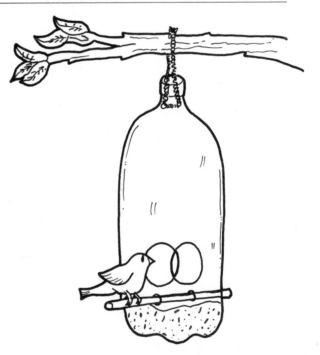

Encourage them to describe the birds that come to the feeder. What color are their feathers? Are they big or small? What sounds do they make?

Extension: Hang a chart near the window and help the children keep track of the number of birds they see.

Wetlands Mural

Materials: Nature magazines; brown butcher paper; blue and green construction paper; tape; pair of scissors.

Preparation: Attach a piece of brown butcher paper to a wall at the children's eye level. Add a blue construction paper stream. Cut pictures of wetlands animals, such as ducks, frogs, otters, beavers, herons and dragonflies, out of nature magazines. Cut pieces of green construction paper as shown to make grass.

Activity: Have each child tape a piece of the construction paper grass to the brown butcher paper to create a wetlands scene. Then let the children select wetlands animal pictures to add to the mural. Encourage them to place the animals where they would be found in the wetlands. For example: ducks swimming in the water, beavers hiding in the grass and dragonflies flying in the air. Name and discuss the different animals with the children. Why do they think those animals like to live in the wetlands?

Wetlands Snack

Ingredients: 2 cups unsweetened apple juice (separated); 1 cup cranberries; extra cranberries for tasting (if desired); 1 envelope plain gelatin; measuring cups; mixing bowl; spoons; blender; clear glass bowl; strainer; gelatin mold; saucepan; stove; refrigerator.

Preparation: Set out the ingredients.

Activity: Tell the children that cranberries grow in wetlands, or bogs as they are sometimes called. Show the children the cranberries. Let them taste the berries, if desired. (Cranberries are very tart when eaten by themselves.) Then let the children help you make cranberry gelatin. Heat 1 cup of apple juice in a saucepan. Pour 1 envelope of plain gelatin a mixing bowl. Add the heated apple juice. Stir the juice until the gelatin is dissolved. Pour the remaining cup of apple juice into a blender container and add 1 cup of cranberries. Whirl the juice and berries together. Set a strainer on top of a glass bowl and pour the juice and berry mixture into it. Add the cranberry liquid to the gelatine mixture. Stir until the mixture is combined. Then pour the liquid into a gelatin mold and refrigerate until firm.

Down in the Wetlands

Sung to: "Down by the Station"

Down in the wetlands
Early in the morning,
See all the ducklings
Swimming in a row.
See the mother duck
Keeping them in line,
Quack, quack, quack, quack,
Off she goes.

Down in the wetlands
Early in the morning,
See all the tadpoles
Swimming in a row.
See the mother frog
Sitting on a lily pad,
Croak, croak, croak, croak,
Off she goes.

Down in the wetlands
Early in the morning,
See the baby otters
Playing in the water.
See the mother otter
Swimming after them,
Swim, swim, swim, swim,
Off she goes.

Down in the wetlands
Early in the morning,
See all the dragonflies
Flying in a row.
See the mother dragonfly
Flying here and there,
Flit, flit, flit, flit,
Off she goes.

Down in the wetlands
Early in the morning,
See the baby herons
With their long necks.
See the mother heron
Fishing for their food,
Fish, fish, fish, fish,
Off she goes.

Down in the wetlands
Early in the morning,
See the baby beavers
Helping build a dam.
See the mother beaver
Busy as can be,
Build, build, build, build,
Off she goes.

Jean Warren

The Food Chain

Materials: 9- by 12-inch pieces of construction paper; magazines; brown felt-tip markers; glue; pair of scissors.

Preparation: Cut pictures of plants and animals out of magazines. Cut pieces of 9- by 12-inch construction paper lengthwise into thirds.

Activity: Give each of the children three strips of construction paper. Have them decorate one of their strips with brown felt-tip markers to represent the soil in the food chain, glue pictures of plants on another of their strips to represent the plants in the food chain, and glue pictures of animals on their last strips to represent the animals in the food chain. Talk about the food chain and its parts while the children are decorating their strips. Tell them that every living plant or animal depends on other plants and animals to survive. This is the food chain. Soil contains parts of decayed plants and animals that nourish seeds and help them grow into plants. The plants are food for animals, and some animals are food for other animals. Then the plants and animals die and decay, making the soil rich for new plants to grow and begin the cycle again. After the children complete their strips, hook the strips together in a large chain. Be sure to keep the strips in order: soil, plants, animals; soil, plants, animals, etc. Hang the chain on a wall or a bulletin board.

Food Chain Song

Sung to: "The Bear Went Over the Mountain"

See the dark brown soil,
See the dark brown soil,
See the dark brown soil,
It's part of the food chain.

See the green healthy plants,
See the green healthy plants,
See the green healthy plants,
They're part of the food chain.

See the hungry animals,
See the hungry animals,
See the hungry animals,
They're part of the food chain.

The food chain needs all three,
The food chain needs all three,
The food chain needs all three,
To make it go around.

Gayle Bittinger

What Is Litter?

Materials: Various kinds of litter, such as a pop can, a gum wrapper, a plastic bag and a piece of paper; objects you would find in nature, such as a leaf, a pine cone, a branch and a rock.

Preparation: None.

Activity: Set out the litter and the nature objects. Tell the children that litter is garbage that someone did not put in a garbage can. Ask them to point to the objects that are litter. How do they know those items are litter? What should they do with them now? Then take other pieces of litter and hide them around the room. Give each of the children a sack and let them hunt around the room for the litter and put it in their sacks.

Extension: Take the children and their sacks outside. Let them pick up litter and throw it away in their sacks. Make sure the children understand that they should not pick up glass or anything else that might hurt them and that they should point those things out to you.

Litter Is Garbage

Sung to: "The Wheels on the Bus"

Litter is garbage that wasn't put away,
Wasn't put away, wasn't put away.
Litter is garbage that wasn't put away,
In the garbage can.

I put my garbage in the garbage can,
The garbage can, the garbage can.
I put my garbage in the garbage can,
I'm not a litterbug.

Gayle Bittinger

Litterbags

Materials: Brown paper lunch bags; sponges; craft knife; shallow containers; tempera paint; yarn; hole punch.

Preparation: Open up brown paper lunch bags and fold down the tops about 1 inch. Use a hole punch to punch two holes on one side of each bag and thread a piece of yarn through them to make a hanger. Close the bags so that they lie flat. Use a craft knife to cut sponges into simple tree and flower shapes. Pour small amounts of tempera paint into shallow containers.

Activity: Give each child one of the paper bags. Have the children use the sponge shapes and paint to print trees and flowers all over their bags. While the children are working, talk about what happens to our land when we litter and why we want to keep our land litter-free. Allow the paint to dry. Open up the bags. Let the children take their litterbags home to use in their rooms or in their families' cars.

Litter-Free Picnic

Materials: Picnic lunch.

Preparation: None.

Activity: Take the children to a park and have a picnic lunch. When the lunch is over, have the children carefully gather up all of their garbage and throw it away in a garbage can. While they are working, let them sing the following song:

Sung to: "Skip to My Lou"

We're not litterbugs, no siree,
We're not litterbugs, no siree,
We're not litterbugs, no siree.
We pick up our trash, you see.

Elizabeth McKinnon

Down at the Dump

Sung to: "Down by the Station"

Down at the dump
Early in the morning,
See the dump trucks
Standing in a row.
See them dump the garbage
In a great big pile,
Dump, dump, dump, dump,
Watch them go.

Pretty soon our dumps
Will all be full,
We had better figure out
Something to do.
We could all recycle
Some of our garbage,
Recycle, recycle,
Watch us go.

Out in the garden
We could make a pile
Of all our food scraps,
So they can decay.
See us dump the scraps
In a great big pile,
Dump, dump, dump, dump,
Watch us go.

Then we could send off
All our cans and jars,
So they can be used
To make some new ones.
See us dump the cans and jars
In a great big bag,
Dump, dump, dump, dump,
Watch us go.

Let's all recycle,
Let's all give a hand,
'Cause if we recycle
We'll have a nicer land.
See us sorting out
All of our garbage,
Sort, sort, sort, sort,
Watch us go.

Jean Warren

Compost Pile Sorting Game

Materials: Magazines; clear self-stick paper; pair of scissors.

Preparation: Cut out magazine pictures of things that go in a compost pile, such as leaves, grass, shrubs, tree branches, straw, fruits, vegetables, coffee grounds, tea leaves and eggshells. Then cut out magazine pictures of things that do not go in a compost pile, such as plastic bags, paper, jars and soap. Cover the pictures with clear self-stick paper for durability.

Activity: Tell the children about compost piles and how they turn some kinds of garbage into a material that can be used to make plants grow bigger and stronger. Then show the children the pictures. Have them help you sort the pictures according to things you can put in a compost pile and things you can't.

Extension: Have the children compost kitchen scraps according to the directions in the Parent Flyer activity "Making Compost" on page 38.

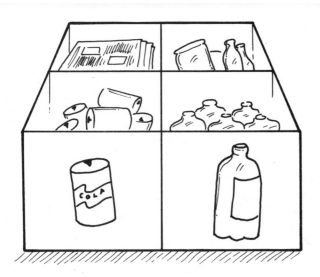

Recyclable Garbage

Materials: Newspapers; empty glass jars and bottles, aluminum cans and plastic soft drink bottles; four cardboard boxes; felt-tip markers.

Preparation: Draw a picture of each of the following on a separate cardboard box: a newspaper, a glass bottle and jar, an aluminum can and a plastic soft drink bottle.

Activity: Set out the labeled boxes and newspapers, empty glass bottles and jars, aluminum cans and plastic soft drink bottles. Let the children take turns sorting the recyclable garbage into the appropriate boxes.

Aluminum Can Crusher

Materials: Two 2-foot sections of 2- by 4-inch wooden studs; hinge; screws; screwdriver; mayonnaise or similar jar lid; hammer; nail; plastic bag or cardboard box.

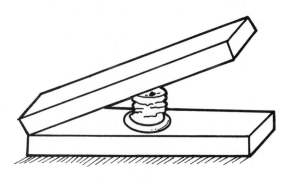

Preparation: Attach a hinge between two 2-foot sections of 2- by 4-inch wooden studs so that the studs stack on top of each other and open and close. Open the studs and nail a mayonnaise jar lid to one of them, about 12 inches from the hinge.

Activity: Let the children take turns using the can crusher to crush aluminum cans. Have them open the studs, place a can in the mayonnaise jar lid and close the studs as far as possible to crush the can. Have them put the crushed cans in a cardboard box or a plastic bag.

Extension: With the children, take the crushed cans to an aluminum can recycling center.

Re-Usable Paper

Materials: Box.

Preparation: None.

Activity: Let the children participate in this on-going project to re-use one of our resources, paper. Place an empty box by the garbage can or in the art area. Have the children put papers in the box that they no longer want and that are only marked on one side. Then encourage the children to look in the re-usable-paper box when they want paper to draw on or to use in art projects.

Recycled Paper

Materials: Newspaper; bowl; measuring cup; water; egg beater; measuring spoons; liquid starch; cake pan; fine-meshed screen to fit in pan (available at hardware stores); blotter paper; rolling pin.

Preparation: None.

Activity: Let the children help you make recycled paper by following the steps listed below.

1. Tear a single page of newspaper into tiny pieces, put them in a bowl and add 2 cups warm water.

2. Beat the paper and water with an egg beater until the mixture turns into pulp. Add 2 teaspoons of liquid starch and mix well.

3. Place a fine-meshed screen in the bottom of a cake pan and pour the pulp into the pan.

4. Lift out the screen, hold it level and let it drain for about 1 minute.

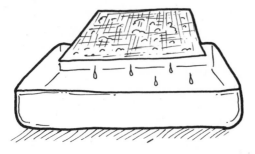

5. Place several newspapers in a pile with a piece of blotter paper on top, then set the screen, pulp side up, on the paper. Put another piece of blotter paper on top of the pulp and more newspapers on top of that.

6. Run a rolling pin over the top of the newspapers to get all the excess water out of the pulp.

7. Carefully take off the top newspapers. Turn all the remaining papers over and remove the newspapers, blotter paper and screen.

8. Put dry blotter paper on top of the pulp. After 24 hours peel off the blotter paper to reveal the recycled paper.

What Can I Do With This?

Materials: Items from the garbage that could be re-used.

Preparation: None.

Activity: Explain to the children that we throw away a lot of garbage. One of the ways we can decrease that amount is to use objects over and over again instead of throwing them away. Give each child an object that ordinarily might have been put in the garbage. Ask each child to describe something he or she could do with the object.

Art With Recyclables

Materials: Any items that might have been thrown away, such as plastic containers and lids, packaging materials, cardboard boxes and containers, fabric and yarn scraps and paper; staplers; tape; glue.

Preparation: Set out the materials.

Activity: Let the children use the recyclable materials any way they wish to create art. Encourage them to arrange and fasten the materials together with glue, tape or staples.

Variation: Have the children work together to create one piece of recyclable art.

Dear Parents,

We are learning about dirt and about the plants and trees that grow in it. Try the following activities with your child and have fun learning more about plants and dirt and growing things.

I Love Dirt

Sung to: "Three Blind Mice"

I love dirt, I love dirt.
Fun, brown dirt; fun, brown dirt.
I love to dig down in the ground,
I love to have dirt all around,
I love to pile it in a mound.
I love dirt.

Gayle Bittinger

Plant Rubbings

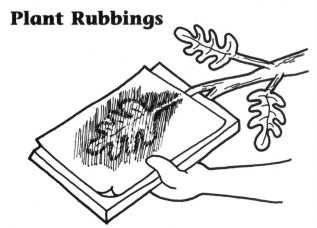

Go outside with your child and take pieces of plain white paper, a crayon and a hard surface to write on. Ask your child to search for interesting plants. When he or she finds one, carefully put one of the leaves or branches of the plant between a sheet of paper and the hard surface and let your child rub the crayon over it. Have your child collect rubbings of several different kinds of plants. Ask him or her to describe how the plants are alike and how they are different.

Mini Garden

Help your child start a mini garden. The garden could be outside in a small section of the yard, or it could be inside in an old flower pot that sits in a sunny window. Let your child choose one or two kinds of seeds he or she wants to plant. Have your child water and take care of his or her garden as it grows.

Dear Parents,

We have been learning about forests and wetlands and the animals that live there. The following activities are ones you can do with your child to help foster a love of the land we live on and the animals we share it with.

Down in the Wetlands
Sung to: "Down by the Station"

Down in the wetlands
Early in the morning,
See the baby herons
With their long necks.
See the mother heron
Fishing for their food,
Fish, fish, fish, fish,
Off she goes.

Down in the wetlands
Early in the morning,
See all the dragonflies
Flying in a row.
See the mother dragonfly
Flying here and there,
Flit, flit, flit, flit,
Off she goes.

Down in the wetlands
Early in the morning,
See the baby beavers
Helping build a dam.
See the mother beaver
Busy as can be,
Build, build, build, build,
Off she goes.

Jean Warren

Orange Cup Bird Feeders

Make this bird feeder with your child. Cut an orange in half. Carefully scoop out all of the fruit. Set the orange cups aside. Let your child help you cut or break the fruit of the orange and several other kinds of fruit, such as apples, bananas and grapes, into small pieces. Have your child fill the orange cups with the pieces of fruit. Let him or her place the cups outside on the ground, on a table or on a tree stump. From inside, observe the birds that come to your orange cups. Encourage your child to count and describe the birds.

Nature Walk

Take your child on a walk through a park or the woods. Walk slowly and stop frequently. Encourage your child to look around carefully. What does he or she see? If you stand quietly in one place, you might have a chance to see a bird or a squirrel. Ask your child to close his or her eyes and listen to the sounds in the park or the woods. What sounds does your child hear? What is making those sounds? Encourage your child to describe what he or she is seeing and hearing.

Dear Parents,

We are learning about what happens to our land when we don't take care of it, and we are learning about some of the things we can do to help. The following song and compost activity are things you and your child can do together to help take care of the land we live on.

Down at the Dump
Sung to: "Down by the Station"

Down at the dump early in the morning,
See the dump trucks standing in a row.
See them dump the garbage
In a great big pile,
Dump, dump, dump, dump,
Watch them go.

Pretty soon our dumps will all be full,
We had better figure out something to do.
We could all recycle
Some of our garbage,
Recycle, recycle,
Watch us go.

Out in the garden we could make a pile
Of our food scraps, so they can decay.
See us dump the scraps
In a great big pile,
Dump, dump, dump, dump,
Watch us go.

Then we could send off all our cans and jars,
So they can be used to make some new ones.
See us dump the cans and jars
In a great big bag,
Dump, dump, dump, dump,
Watch us go.

Let's all recycle let's all give a hand,
'Cause if we recycle we'll have a nicer
    land.
See us sorting out
All of our garbage,
Sort, sort, sort, sort,
Watch us go

Jean Warren

Making Compost

Help your child cut up the food scraps from a meal into small pieces. Drain any excess liquid. Have your child spread the food pieces across the bottom of a leakproof container, then cover them with a thin layer of soil. Each day let your child stir the mixture, then add another layer of chopped-up food scraps and another layer of soil. Continue until the mixture is 3 to 4 inches deep. Have your child stir the mixture every day for the next three weeks, adding a few drops of water if it appears to be drying out. Your food is now composted and the mixture can be added to the soil in gardens and around house plants.

Dear Parents,

We are learning about the importance of recycling and re-using materials to help use our resources more wisely. The following suggestions are things you can do with your child to recycle and re-use some of our resources.

Sorting Recyclable Garbage

Collect all of your recyclable garbage such as aluminum cans, plastic soft drink bottles, tin cans, glass jars and cardboard in one box. Help your child sort the garbage into separate piles. (Hint: Have your child wear gloves to protect his or her hands.)

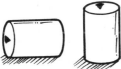

Checklist for Helping

You and your child may want to consider doing one, two or all of these suggestions together to help use our resources more efficiently.

☑ Say, "No bag, please" at stores when buying one or two items. Bring your own bag when you are purchasing many things.

☑ Write or draw on both sides of a piece of paper before recycling it.

☑ Recycle as many items as you can, including paper, aluminum, tin, glass and plastic.

☑ Use plastic bags more than once.

☑ Use dishes and re-usable cups instead of throwaway dishes and cups.

Re-Using Materials

Make games such as the following out of re-usable materials:

Use plastic soft drink bottles and a rubber ball to make a bowling game.

Cut the centers out of plastic lids to make rings for playing ring toss.

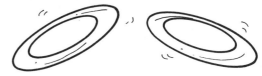

Make a sand scoop by cutting off, at an angle, the end of a bleach bottle. (Smooth rough edges.)

Cut the tops off pairs of cardboard milk cartons and put each pair together to make a block.

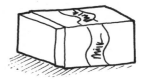

OUR AIR

Balloons and Air

Materials: Balloons.

Preparation: None.

Activity: Show the children a balloon that is blown up and a balloon that is not. Ask them why the balloons look different. (One has air in it.) Then blow up a balloon and let it go. Why does it fly around the room? How far does it go? Blow up a balloon partway and another balloon all the way. Ask the children which balloon will fly farther. Why?

Air Takes Up Space

Materials: Clear bowl; tall clear glass; paper napkin; water.

Preparation: Fill a clear bowl with water.

Activity: Ask a child to crumple a paper napkin and place it in the bottom of a tall clear glass. Have the children observe while you turn the glass upside down and, keeping it level, lower it into the bowl of water. What is happening in the glass? Why isn't the water going into the glass? Lift the glass out of the water and take out the napkin. Why is it dry? (The glass was filled with air so there was no room for the water to get in.)

Experiments With Air

Materials: Cotton balls; straws; paper scraps.

Preparation: None.

Activity: Give each child a straw, a cotton ball and a scrap of paper. Let the children experiment with the items to answer the following questions: Can you feel air? (Blow air through a straw against your hand.) Can you make a cotton ball move without touching it? (Blow on it.) Can you pick up a small piece of paper with a straw? (Hold the straw against the paper and suck on the straw.)

Wind Hummers

Materials: Plastic lids; nail; yarn; pair of scissors.

Preparation: For each child make a flat plastic circle by cutting the rim off a plastic lid. Use a nail to punch two holes, 1 inch apart, in the center of the circle. Thread a 16-inch piece of string through the holes and tie the ends together to create a wind hummer.

Activity: Give each child a wind hummer. Show the children how to "wind up" their circles by moving their strings in a circular motion. Then show them how to pull their strings tight to make their circles hum. The sound that their wind hummers make is like the sound the wind makes when it blows.

Air Painting

Materials: Straws; spoon; tempera paint; construction paper; straight pin.

Preparation: Use a straight pin to poke one or two holes near one end of a straw. Repeat for each child. Set out tempera paint and construction paper.

Activity: Give each child a straw and a piece of construction paper. Spoon a little tempera paint on each child's paper. Let the children practice blowing air out of their mouths. Encourage them put their hands in front of their mouths to feel the air coming out. Then have them blow through their straws to move the paint around on their papers. (The holes in the straws help prevent the paint from being inhaled in case a child breathes in instead of out.)

It Is Air

Sung to: "Frere Jacques"

You can't see it, you can't see it,
But it's there, everywhere.
It fills up balloons,
It takes up space.
It is air, it is air.

You can't see it, you can't see it,
But it's there, everywhere.
It makes things move
When it blows.
It is air, it is air.

You can't see it, you can't see it,
But it's there, everywhere.
It makes loud noises,
As it rushes by us.
It is air, it is air.

Gayle Bittinger

Wind Facts

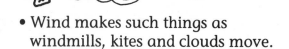

Material: None.

Preparation: None.

Activity: Share these facts about wind with the children:

• Air cannot be seen, but it is all around us.

• Wind is air that is moving fast.

• Wind makes such things as windmills, kites and clouds move.

• Wind is an important part of our weather.

• A weather vane shows which way the wind is blowing.

Windsocks

Materials: Oatmeal or salt boxes; construction paper; pair of scissors; felt-tip markers; crepe paper; glue; stapler; hole punch; string.

Preparation: Cut the tops and bottoms off oatmeal or salt boxes. Cut construction paper to fit around each box. Cut crepe paper into 6-inch strips.

Activity: Give each child an oatmeal box or a salt box and a precut piece of construction paper. Let the children decorate their papers with felt-tip markers. Help them glue their papers to the outsides of their boxes. Have the children glue or staple the strips of crepe paper around the bottom edges of their boxes. To hang, punch four holes in the top of each box. Lace a string knotted at one end through each hole and tie the four loose ends together.

Variation: Have the children attach crepe paper strips around the edges of paper plates. Tie a string through a hole in the middle of each plate and hang.

I See the Wind

Sung to: "Hush Little Baby"

I see the wind
When the leaves dance by.
I see the wind
When the clothes wave "Hi!"
I see the wind
When the trees bend low.
I see the wind
When the flags all blow.

I see the wind
When the kites fly high.
I see the wind
When the clouds float by.
I see the wind
When it blows my hair.
I see the wind
Most everywhere!

Jean Warren

Moving in the Wind

Materials: Crepe paper; pair of scissors.

Preparation: Cut crepe paper into 18-inch streamers.

Activity: Give the children the crepe paper streamers to hold in their hands. Let them take turns racing across the room and flapping their streamers as if there were strong winds in the room. Then have them walk back across the room, gently waving their streamers as if there were soft breezes in the room.

Plants Give Off Oxygen

Materials: Anacharis (a water plant found in aquarium supply stores); tall clear glass; water.

Preparation: Fill a tall clear glass with water.

Activity: Submerge the anacharis in the glass of water. Have the children observe the plant as bubbles form on its leaves. Ask the children if they know what those bubbles are. (The bubbles are the oxygen that the plant is giving off.) Explain that oxygen is what people and animals need in order to breathe.

People and Plants
Sung to: "Old MacDonald Had a Farm"

People breathe in oxygen
From the air around.
Every time we take a breath
Oxygen goes down.
With a breath, breath here,
And a breath, breath there,
Here a breath, there a breath,
Everywhere a breath, breath.
People breathe in oxygen
From the air around.

Oxygen comes from our plants
And goes into the air.
That is why we are so glad
Plants are everywhere.
With a breath, breath here,
And a breath, breath there,
Here a breath, there a breath,
Everywhere a breath, breath.
Oxygen comes from our plants
And goes into the air.

Gayle Bittinger

Plant a Tree

Materials: Tin cans; spades or shovels.

Preparation: Find an area filled with seedlings. Get permission for the children to dig up some of them for this activity.

Activity: Explain to the children that we need trees to clean our air. The trees take in the carbon dioxide we breathe out and they produce the oxygen that we breathe in. Then take the children to the place that has tree seedlings. Give them each a tin can. Ask them to find a seedling that they would like to take home and plant. Let them use the spades to carefully dig up their seedlings and put them in their tin cans. The seedlings will take a long time to grow, but someday they will be tall trees that take in lots of carbon dioxide and produce lots of oxygen.

Variation: Instead of planting seedlings outdoors, have the children grow houseplants for indoors.

The Air Cycle

Materials: Magazines; clear self-stick paper; yarn; construction paper; pen; hole punch; pair of scissors.

Preparation: Cut pictures of people and pictures plants out of magazines. Cover each picture with clear self-stick paper, punch a hole in it and string it on a yarn necklace. Make people necklaces for half the children and plant necklaces for the other half. Cut a circle out of construction paper and write the word "air" on it.

Activity: Let the children each select a necklace. Have the children with plant necklaces line up on one side of the room and the children with people necklaces line up across from them on the other side. Explain to the children that people breathe in oxygen and breathe out carbon dioxide. Then tell them that plants take in carbon dioxide and put out oxygen. Demonstrate this cycle by giving the first child in the people necklace line the circle with "air" written on it. Have the child take the pretend air to the first child in the plant necklace line and sit down. Have the child with the plant necklace take the pretend air to the next child in the people necklace line. Continue the cycle until each child has had a chance to carry the air to the other group.

Air Pollution

Materials: Flashlight.

Preparation: None.

Activity: Have the children sit in a circle. Ask them if they think there is anything in the air around them. Then turn out the lights and shine a flashlight in front of the children. Can they see tiny particles in the air now? Explain that air pollution occurs when there are too many of these particles in the air.

Collecting Air Pollution

Materials: Index cards; petroleum jelly; felt-tip markers; tape.

Preparation: Write each child's name on a separate index card.

Activity: Give each child the index card with his or her name on it. Have the children use their fingers to spread petroleum jelly on their cards. Then let them choose places to hang up their cards to collect air particles. Make sure that some of the cards are hung up outside and some inside. Leave the cards in place for one week. Let the children collect their cards. Have them compare the different amounts of particles on their cards. Which cards have the most particles? Which have the least? Where is there the most pollution?

Extension: Let the children examine the particles on their cards with magnifying glasses.

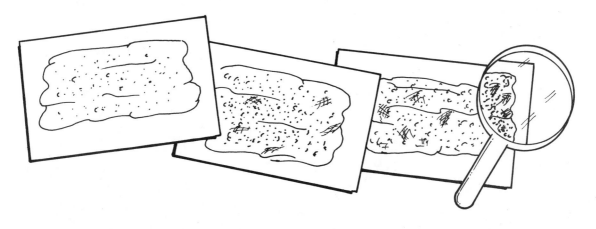

More Air Pollution

Materials: White ceramic tile (individual tiles are available at home decorating centers); candle; matches; tongs or pliers.

Preparation: None.

Activity: Place the candle on a table and have the children sit where they can see it. Light the candle. Ask the children if they can see any pollution coming up from the candle. Then hold a white ceramic tile with a pair of tongs or pliers and barely touch it to the candle flame. What is left on the tile? (Soot.) Where does the soot go when it doesn't land on the tile? What would happen if there were a lot of candles or a fire burning?

Caution: Activities using lighted candles require adult supervision at all times.

Air Pollution Detectives

Materials: None.

Preparation: None.

Activity: Take the children outside for a walk. Ask them to be detectives and to look carefully for causes of air pollution. What kinds of things cause air pollution in their neighborhood?

Cars and Fuel

Materials: None.

Preparation: None.

Activity: Explain to the children that cars that use gasoline give off a lot of pollution and that most cars today still use gasoline. Ask them to pretend to be scientists. What would they use to make cars go? Then sing the following song, inserting a different answer in the blank each time.

Sung to: "Little White Duck"

When cars with gasoline go, go, go,
They give off pollution, this we know.
So I'll invent a car someday
That runs on _____ and then I'll say
Now there's no more pollution in
   the air
With my car.

Gayle Bittinger

Take the Bus

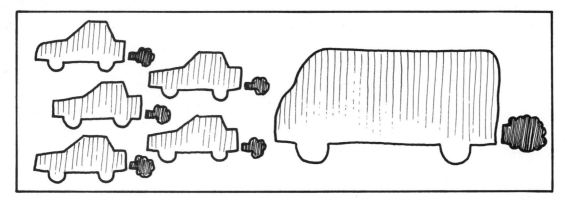

Materials: Flannelboard; felt scraps; pair of scissors.

Preparation: Cut several car shapes and the same number of small exhaust shapes out of felt. Then cut a bus shape and a medium exhaust cloud shape out of felt.

Activity: Place one of the car shapes and the bus shape on a flannelboard. Put one of the small exhaust shapes behind the car and the medium exhaust shape behind the bus. Ask the children: "If just one person were riding in the car or in the bus, which vehicle would keep our air cleaner and be better to drive? Why?" Then place the remaining car shapes on the flannelboard and add the small exhaust cloud shapes. Now have the children compare the amount of pollution created. Which gives off more pollution, all of the cars or one bus? Which would be better for our air, lots of people driving lots of cars or lots of people riding one bus?

Soot, Soot, Soot

Sung to: "Three Blind Mice"

Look, look, look; look, look, look.
Soot, soot, soot; soot, soot, soot.
The air is filled with soot today,
It covers the buildings, it covers the
   bay.
I wish pollution would go away.
Soot, soot, soot.

Help, help, help; help, help, help.
We can help, we can help.
We can burn everything quite care-
   fully,
We can drive our cars more thought-
   fully,
To clean up our air so beautifully.
We can help.

Jean Warren

Noise Pollution

Materials: Tape recorder; cassette tape.

Preparation: Use a tape recorder to record sounds on a busy street corner and sounds in a quiet park or forest.

Activity: Explain to the children that you are going to demonstrate another kind of pollution that is carried in the air: noise pollution. Play the recorded sounds from the street corner. Then play the sounds from the park or forest. Can the children identify some of the sounds from each place? Which sounds did they like best? What could be done to make the street corner quieter?

Dear Parents,

We have been learning about air and what it does. We have also been learning about the wind and the part it plays in our weather. Try the following activities with your child to learn more about the air around us.

It Is Air
Sung to: "Frere Jacques"

You can't see it, you can't see it,
But it's there, everywhere.
It fills up balloons,
It takes up space.
It is air, it is air.

You can't see it, you can't see it,
But it's there, everywhere.
It makes things move
When it blows.
It is air, it is air.

You can't see it, you can't see it,
But it's there, everywhere.
It makes loud noises,
As it rushes by us.
It is air, it is air.

Gayle Bittinger

Wind Game

Collect a variety of nonbreakable objects of various weights, such as a cotton ball, a pencil, a small book and a paperweight. Place one of the objects on a smooth surface such as a tiled floor or a tabletop. Have your child pretend to be the wind and try blowing the object across the floor or table. How much wind does it take to move a cotton ball? How much wind does it take to move a book? Can a paperweight be moved by the wind? Why not?

Milk Carton Wind Catcher

Cut a vertical "door" in each side of a milk carton. (Make sure the doors are cut so that they will all open in the same direction.) Fold the doors open and let your child paint the carton with a powder tempera paint and liquid soap mixture. Punch a hole in the top of the carton and tie a piece of string through it. Hang the finished wind catcher outside and watch it twirl.

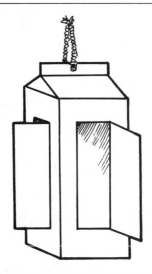

Dear Parents,

We have been learning about air pollution and how to take care of the air. We have also learned that plants give off the oxygen that we breathe. The activities below are things you can do with your child to learn more about how the air gets dirty and how we can help keep it clean.

Plants, Plants, Everywhere

Plants help keep our air clean. They take in carbon dioxide and produce oxygen that people and animals breathe. Take your child on a walk outside. How many different kinds of plants can he or she find? Which one is the tallest? The shortest? How many different colors of plants can your child see? If you have plants indoors, have your child count them. Let your child take care of a plant purchased or brought in from outside.

Dusting Away Pollution

Let your child help you dust. Look at the furniture carefully before you start. Ask your child to describe what he or she sees. Where did the dust come from? (The air.) Why is there dust in our air? Then let your child dust the pollution away.

Extension: Make your own furniture polish by combining 2 tablespoons lemon juice with 1/2 cup mineral oil. Apply with a clean rag.

Soot, Soot, Soot
Sung to: "Three Blind Mice"

Look, look, look; look, look, look.
Soot, soot, soot; soot, soot, soot.
The air is filled with soot today,
It covers the buildings, it covers the bay.
I wish pollution would go away.
Soot, soot, soot.

Help, help, help; help, help, help.
We can help, we can help.
We can burn everything quite carefully,
We can drive our cars more
  thoughtfully,
To clean up our air so beautifully.
We can help.

Jean Warren

OUR WATER

Water Fun

Materials: Plastic containers such as margarine tubs, juice bottles or whipped topping tubs; dishpans; nail; water.

Preparation: Fill dishpans with water.

Activity: Give the children the plastic containers and let them experiment with pouring and measuring the water in the dishpans. Then poke holes in some of the containers with a nail, varying the number and size of the holes. Encourage the children to observe, discuss and explore what happens with the different containers.

Variation: Set out plastic measuring cups, colanders, spoons and ladles for the children to experiment with.

Water Song

Sung to: "The Wheels on the Bus"

Water is wet and it pours like this,
Pours like this, pours like this.
Water is wet and it pours like this,
See how it goes.

Water is liquid and it sprinkles
   like this,
Sprinkles like this, sprinkles like this.
Water is liquid and it sprinkles
   like this,
See how it goes.

Water is clear and it bubbles like
   this,
Bubbles like this, bubbles like this.
Water is clear and it bubbles like
   this,
See how it goes.

Let the children pour water, sprinkle water and make bubbles in water while they sing this song.

Gayle Bittinger

Making Bubbles

Materials: Dry sponges of various kinds and sizes; dishpans; water.

Preparation: Fill dishpans with water and put them on a table. Set out a variety of kinds and sizes of dry sponges.

Activity: Let the children take turns placing the sponges in the dishpans. Have them observe as bubbles appear on the sponges and float to the top of the water. Do different sponges make different sized bubbles? Which makes more bubbles, a wet sponge or a dry sponge? Where do the bubbles come from? (The water moves into the dry sponges, forcing the air inside to come out and form bubbles.)

Exploring With Ice

Materials: Balloons; freezer; dishpans; water; pair of scissors.

Preparation: Fill balloons partway with water and put them in a freezer until the water is frozen. Take the ice-filled balloons out of the freezer, then cut and peel off the balloons to reveal the unusual shapes of ice. Put the ice shapes in dishpans filled with water.

Activity: Let the children play with the water and the ice shapes. Ask them to observe the ice. Do the ice shapes float? Are parts of the ice shapes above or below the water? What is happening to the temperature of the water in the dishpans? Why?

What Is Ice?

Sung to: "Frere Jacques"

What is ice? What is ice?
Do you know? Do you know?
It is water that's been
Cooled until it's frozen.
That is ice. That is ice.

Gayle Bittinger

Disappearing Water

Materials: Clear plastic cups; permanent felt-tip marker; small pitchers; water.

Preparation: For each child use a permanent felt-tip marker to mark a line and write the child's name on a clear plastic cup. Fill small pitchers with water.

Activity: Give each child his or her cup and set out the water pitchers. Have the children use the water pitchers to fill their cups up to the lines. Let them place their cups around the room. Have them observe their cups of water over the next several days. What is happening to the water levels? Where is the water going? Explain to the children that the water is evaporating. Evaporation occurs when particles of water become warm enough to turn into a vapor and escape into the air. How could the children make the water in their cups evaporate faster?

Droplet Designs

Materials: Eyedroppers; paper towels; food coloring; paper cups; water.

Preparation: Fill several paper cups with water and add food coloring to each one.

Activity: Give each child an eyedropper and a paper towel. Let the children create droplet designs on their towels by using their eyedroppers to drop colored water on them. Do their towels feel wet or dry? Have the children wait a few minutes. Now how do their towels feel? What happened to the water? (It evaporated.)

Evaporation Experiment

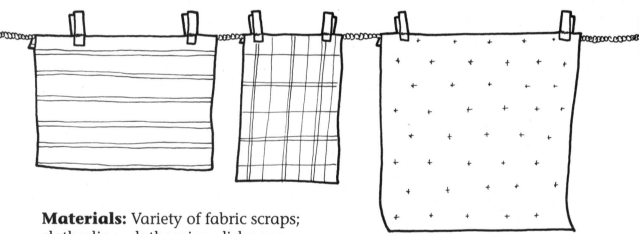

Materials: Variety of fabric scraps; clothesline; clothespins; dishpans; water.

Preparation: Hang up a clothesline at the children's level and clip clothespins to it. Fill dishpans with water and set them on a table with scraps of different kinds of fabric.

Activity: Let the children each select a fabric scrap. Let them get their fabric scraps wet in the dishpans, wring the water from them and hang them up on the clothesline. Have the children observe their fabric scraps throughout the day. What is happening to the water in their fabric? Where is the water going? Which fabric scrap dried first?

Condensation

Materials: Two jars and their lids; ice water; room-temperature water.

Preparation: Fill a jar with ice water and another jar with room-temperature warm water. Screw their lids on tightly. Set the jars on a table.

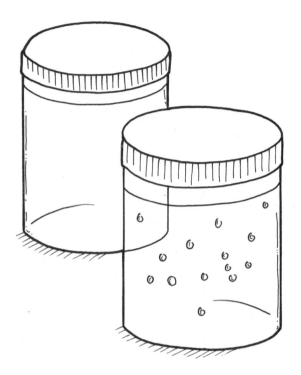

Activity: Show the children the jars. Ask them to describe what is happening to the outsides of the jars. Point out that only the jar with ice water inside has drops of water on the outside. This is called condensation. Condensation happens when the water particles in the air become cold enough to change into drops of water.

Absorption

Materials: A variety of materials that will absorb water, such as fabric, cotton balls and newspaper; a variety of materials that will not absorb water, such as plastic, Styrofoam and aluminum foil; eyedroppers; small paper cups; water; pair of scissors.

Preparation: Cut or tear the absorbent and non-absorbent

materials into small pieces. Fill small paper cups with water.

Activity: Give each child a small piece of each kind of material, a cup of water and an eyedropper. Let the children put several drops of water on each of their material pieces and observe what happens. What material absorbs water best? What materials do not absorb water at all?

Extension: Ask the children which material they think would be the best for cleaning up a puddle of water. Then spill a little water on a table and let them test their answers.

Absorption Song

Sung to: "The Mulberry Bush"

What happens to water that's spilled on paper,
Spilled on paper, spilled on paper?
What happens to water that's spilled on paper?
It is absorbed.

What happens to water that's spilled on foil,
Spilled on foil, spilled on foil?
What happens to water that's spilled on foil?
It is not absorbed.

Sing the appropriate verse of the song for
each material the children experiment with.

Gayle Bittinger

Water Charades

Materials: Index cards; felt tip markers; pair of scissors.

Preparation: Draw simple pictures of different activities you can do in or with water, such as swimming, brushing teeth and watering plants, on index cards.

Activity: Put the water activity cards in a pile. Have the children sit in a circle. Ask one child to stand up, select one of the cards and, without showing it to anyone, act out the movement pictured on the card. Have the other children try to guess what activity he or she is acting out. Let the child who guesses correctly have the next turn or choose another child to be next. Continue until each child has had a turn.

Rain Gauge

Materials: Clear glass jar; permanent felt-tip marker; ruler.

Preparation: Make a rain gauge by using a permanent felt-tip marker and a ruler to mark inches or centimeters on the outside of a clear glass jar.

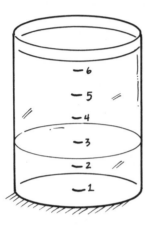

Activity: Show the children the rain gauge. Explain to them that when it rains, drops will fall into the jar, allowing them to measure how much rain fell. Have the children help you select a place outside for the rain gauge. Make sure the gauge is positioned securely. Then after the next rainfall, take the children outside to check the gauge. How much rain fell? What does the rain look like? Leave the gauge outside to collect the rain that falls over a period of time such as a week or a month.

Extension: Make a graph and keep track of the amount of rain that falls each time.

Rain Book

Materials: Magazines or seed catalogs; white paper; felt-tip marker; stapler; glue.

Preparation: Staple four to six pieces of white paper together for each child. Use a felt-tip marker to write the words "Rain Helps Things Grow" on the first page of each book.

Activity: Let the children look through magazines or seed catalogs and tear out pictures of things that need rain to help them grow, such as trees, flowers and other plants. Then have the children glue the pictures in their books. Let the children "read" their books to you by naming the things in the pictures.

Rain Painting

Materials: Paper plates; food coloring or powder tempera paint.

Preparation: None.

Activity: On a rainy day give each child a paper plate. Let the children sprinkle drops of food coloring or small amounts of powder tempera paint on their plates. Have them put on raincoats, walk outside, and hold their plates in the rain for about a minute. After they bring their plates inside, talk about the designs created by the rain.

Rain Song
Sung to: "Frere Jacques"

It is raining, it is raining,
On my head, on my head.
Pitter, pitter, pat, pat,
Pitter, pitter, pat, pat.
Now I'm wet, now I'm wet.

It is raining, it is raining,
On the plants, on the plants.
Pitter, pitter pat, pat,
Pitter, pitter, pat, pat.
Now they'll grow, now they'll grow.

It is raining, it is raining,
On the dirt, on the dirt.
Pitter, pitter, pat, pat,
Pitter, pitter, pat, pat.
Now there's mud, now there's mud.

Gayle Bittinger

Making Rain

Materials: Saucepan; stove or hot plate; pie pan; hot pad; ice cubes; water.

Preparation: Fill a saucepan with water and bring it to a boil over a stove or a hot plate. Fill a pie pan with ice cubes.

Activity: Have the children stand or sit where they can see the pan of boiling water and the steam that is forming above it. Use a hot pad to hold the pie pan filled with ice cubes over the steam "cloud." Have the children observe that when the steam comes in contact with the cool air from the pie pan, drops of water form and fall back into the saucepan like rain. This is similar to the way rain is really made.

Caution: Adults should always supervise activities that require electrical appliances.

The Rain Cycle

Materials: Index cards; felt-tip markers.

Preparation: Draw each of the following scenes on a separate index card: rain storm, creek, river, ocean or lake, blue sky, clouds.

Activity: Show the children the picture cards as you explain the rain cycle. Raindrops fall down and after traveling long distances in small creeks, they eventually end up in a river. The river flows to an ocean or a lake where the raindrops collect and then evaporate into the air. (Evaporation happens when particles of water get warm enough to become vapor and escape into the air.) The vapor in the air gets cold and turns into a cloud, filled with raindrops ready to fall all over again.

Extension: Mix up the picture cards and let the children take turns putting them in sequence and telling the story of the rain cycle.

Variation: Instead of drawing scenes, cut the appropriate pictures out of magazines and glue them each to a separate card.

Rain Cycle Movement

Materials: None.

Preparation: None.

Activity: Let the children act out the rain cycle. Have them pretend to be raindrops that have just fallen. Then give them directions such as these: "The raindrops are joining together to form small streams that move slowly through the countryside. As the streams flow together, they become a wide river moving faster and faster toward the sea. Now all the raindrops are part of the ocean, rolling and swaying in big waves. Out comes the sun, sending hot rays down to the sea. The little raindrops are growing warmer and warmer. One by one, they are turning into vapor and rising up into the sky. Now they join together to form a rain cloud, waiting to fall back down to earth once more."

We Are Little Raindrops

Sung to: "I'm a Little Teapot"

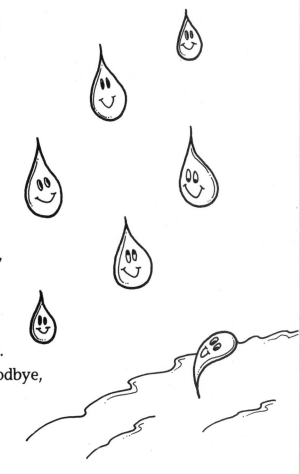

We are little raindrops, watch us fall,
From clouds to ground, one and all.
Watch us as we get together to be
A big water puddle for you to see.

We are in the puddles, see us flow
Into the rivers, now here we go.
Watch us as we move right out to the sea,
A part of the ocean we soon will be.

We are in the ocean oh, so blue,
We float around like raindrops should do.
Soon we'll get all warmed up and say goodbye,
And join more raindrops in the sky.

Gayle Bittinger

Plants and the Rain Cycle

Materials: Plant; clear plastic bag; Popsicle sticks (if needed).

Preparation: None.

Activity: Cover a plant with a clear plastic bag. Use Popsicle sticks, if necessary, to keep the plastic from touching the plant. Set the plant in the sun. Have the children observe the plant in about 30 minutes. What do they see? What is on the plant and the inside of the bag? (Water.) Where did the water come from? Plants take up water through their roots and then give the water off through their leaves. Explain to the children that not all raindrops end up in the ocean. Some of them are collected by plants and used in this way.

Terrariums

Materials: Clear plastic cups; eyedroppers; small rocks; soil; small plants; water; tape.

Preparation: Set out the materials.

Activity: Give each child a clear plastic cup. Have the children each add a layer of rocks and 2 inches of soil to their cups. Let them each choose one or two small plants and put them in the soil. Have the children use eyedroppers to add small amounts of water. Help each child tape a second cup to the top of the his or her first cup to make a terrarium. Have the children observe their terrariums over the next week or so. Ask them if they can see the drops of water forming on top of their terrariums. Where did the water come from?

Rain Cycle Song

Sung to: "The Farmer in the Dell"

Rain comes falling down,
Rain comes falling down,
Rain falls down upon the ground.
Rain comes falling down.

Roots soak up the rain,
Roots soak up the rain,
Roots say "Thanks for rain today."
Roots soak up the rain.

Plants use rain to grow,
Plants use rain to grow,
Plants grow tall when rain does fall.
Plants use rain to grow.

Leaves let out the rain,
Leaves let out the rain,
Leaves let rain out, there is no doubt.
Leaves let out the rain.

The rain turns into vapor,
The rain turns into vapor,
The vapor goes high to make clouds
   in the sky.
The rain turns into vapor.

Gayle Bittinger

How Lakes Are Made

Materials: Round cake pan or pie pan; dirt; pitcher; water.

Preparation: Fill a round cake pan or pie pan with dirt. Fill a pitcher with water.

Activity: Show the children the pan of dirt. Slowly add water or "rain" to the dirt until it is saturated but not overflowing. Dig a small hole in the middle of the pan. Ask the children if they can guess what is going to happen to the hole. Can they see the water flowing into it? In about ten minutes the hole will be completely filled with water. This is how lakes are made. Rain falls down on the land and eventually collects in holes in the ground.

Extension: Take the children outside when the ground is fairly dry. Ask them to guess where puddles or "lakes" might form after it rains. Then go outside after a rainy day. Did puddles form where the children guessed they would?

Down by the Lake

Sung to: "Down by the Station"

Down by the lake early in the morning,
See the little fish swimming by our boat.
See them swish their tails all across the lake,
Swish, swish, swish, swish, off they go.

Jean Warren

Let's Go Fishing

Materials: Dowel, paper towel tube or wooden spoon; small magnet; 3 feet of string; paper clips; construction paper; pair of scissors.

Preparation: Make a fishing pole by tying 3 feet of string to a dowel, a paper towel tube or a wooden spoon. Attach a small magnet to the end of the string. Cut fish shapes from different colors of construction paper and attach a paper clip to each fish.

Activity: Lay the fish shapes out on the floor. Then let the children take turns catching all the red fish, then all the blue fish, etc.

Observing Fish

Materials: Aquarium or fish bowl; water; fish; fish food; posterboard; felt-tip markers.

Preparation: Fill an aquarium or fish bowl with water and add two or three fish. (Check your local pet store for suggestions and guidelines.) Make a poster that shows the parts of a fish including the body, eyes, fins, gills and tail. Hang the poster above the aquarium.

Activity: Discuss the proper care of fish. Show the children the fish in your aquarium and let them take turns feeding the fish. Have the children observe the fish and draw pictures of their observations.

Discuss their findings. How do fish swim? What are their gills used for? Do fish sleep? What happens when you put fish food in the aquarium?

Ocean Waves

Materials: Plastic jar and lid; water; mineral oil; blue food coloring.

Preparation: Fill a plastic jar two-thirds full of water. Add a few drops of blue food coloring. Fill the jar to the top with mineral oil. Screw the jar lid on tightly.

Activity: Have the children take turns holding the bottle sideways and tipping it back and forth to create waves like the waves at the ocean.

Ocean Warm-Up

Materials: None.

Preparation: None.

Activity: Invite the children to join you for some fun in the ocean. Pass out imaginary scuba masks and have the children pretend to put them on and dive under the water. What do they see? Have the children name different things they might see underwater in the ocean, such as fish, seaweed, sharks, whales and octopuses. Have some of the children pretend to be seaweed swaying back and forth in the ocean while the other children pretend to be different ocean animals moving around the seaweed.

I Live in the Ocean

Materials: None.

Preparation: None.

Activity: Discuss with the children animals that live in the ocean and animals that do not. Then say the name of an animal. If the animal lives in the ocean, have the children make wave motions with their hands. If the animal does not live in the ocean, have them keep their hands in their laps.

Pollution in the Rain

Materials: Coffee filters; clean jars or cans; bowls; magnifying glasses.

Preparation: None.

Activity: Give each pair of children a clean jar or can. Have the children set their jars outside when rain is expected. After the rain has fallen, let the children collect their jars and bring them inside. Give each pair of children a coffee filter, a bowl and a magnifying glass. Have one child in each pair hold the coffee filter over the bowl as the other child carefully pours the rainwater into the filter. The filter will catch particles that are in the rain. Let the children observe the

particles on their filters with their magnifying glasses. Where did the particles come from? What might happen if those particles got in streams or lakes?

Dirty Water

Materials: Coffee filters; clear glass or plastic jars with lids; bowls; felt-tip marker.

Preparation: None.

Activity: Take the children on a walk outside to look for places where water has collected. Bring along clear glass or plastic jars with lids. Let the children help put a little water from each source in a different jar. Label each jar according to where the water was found and what type of water it was (puddle, stream, lake, etc.). Take the jars back to the room. Have the children look at the water in the jars. Can they see any differences? Set out bowls and put a coffee filter in each one. Have the children work in pairs to pour the water from each jar through a different filter. Let them use magnifying glasses to examine the particles left on the filters.

What's in the Water?

Materials: Three bowls; vegetable oil; liquid soap; water.

Preparation: Fill three bowls with water. Add vegetable oil to one bowl and liquid soap to another. Leave one bowl as is. Set out the bowls.

Activity: Let the children feel the water in the bowls. Ask them to describe what they are feeling. What is in each bowl? Which bowl would fish like to swim in? Explain to them that oil and soap are two kinds of things that get into the water and pollute it.

Oil Spill

Materials: Pie pans or cake pans; water; vegetable oil; objects for trying to remove oil, such as spoons, cotton balls, fabric scraps, aluminum foil, plastic netting and Popsicle sticks.

Preparation: Place a pie pan or cake pan on a table for each child. Fill the pans halfway with water. Set out the oil removal objects.

Activity: Explain to the children that one of the ways our water gets polluted is when oil is spilled or dumped into it. Have them each sit by a pan and pretend that it is a lake, ocean or river. Ask the children to guess what will happen when you pour oil on their water. Then pour a 1/8-inch layer of vegetable oil on top of the water in each pan. Have them use the objects on the table, or any others they can think of, to try removing the oil from the water. What is happening to the oil and water? Is it easy or hard to remove the oil? If there were animals living in the water, what would be happening to them?

Water Pollution

Materials: Cardboard box; various kinds of garbage such as a plastic bag, a plastic bottle, a newspaper, an aluminum can, a glass jar.

Preparation: Fill a cardboard box with various kinds of garbage (see above).

Activity: Explain to the children that when people litter some of their garbage ends up in our lakes, rivers and oceans. This garbage makes our water dirty, and it can also hurt the fish and other animals that live there. Then set out the box you prepared. Tell the children that this box is filled with some of the kinds of garbage that ends up in our water. Ask one of the children to take a piece of garbage out of the box and identify it. Then sing the song below, inserting the name of the piece of garbage in the blanks. Repeat until each child has had a turn taking out a piece of garbage. After the children have all had turns, let them throw their garbage away in a trash can.

Sung to: "The Bear Went Over the Mountain"

There's something polluting our water,
There's something polluting our water,
There's something polluting our water,
I'll tell you what it is.

It is a _____,
It is a _____,
It is a _____,
Yucky, yucky, poo.
        (Hold nose.)

Jean Warren

I'm Not a Water Hog

Sung to: "Skip to My Lou"

Everybody uses water,
Everybody uses water,
Everybody uses water,
Just don't be a water hog.

I wash my hair with water,
I wash my hair with water,
I wash my hair with water,
But I'm not a water hog.

I keep my grass green with water,
I keep my grass green with water,
I keep my grass green with water,
But I'm not a water hog.

I rinse my dishes with water,
I rinse my dishes with water,
I rinse my dishes with water,
But I'm not a water hog.

Additional verses: Let the children name
other things they use water for.

Jean Warren

Dear Parents,

We have been learning about water: what it feels like, what it looks like and what it does. The activities that follow are things you can do with your child to explore and learn more about water.

Water Song
Sung to: "The Wheels on the Bus"

Water is wet and it pours like this,
Pours like this, pours like this.
Water is wet and it pours like this,
See how it goes.

Water is liquid and it sprinkles like this,
Sprinkles like this, sprinkles like this.
Water is liquid and it sprinkles like this,
See how it goes.

Water is clear and it bubbles like this,
Bubbles like this, bubbles like this.
Water is clear and it bubbles like this,
See how it goes.

Gayle Bittinger

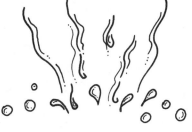

Water Bubbles

Collect three or four plastic bottles with different sizes of openings. At bath time, give your child the bottles and show him or her how to make water bubbles with them. (One way is to lay the bottles on top of the water on their sides and push them down into the water.) Where do the bubbles come from? (Bubbles are made when the air inside the bottles comes out.) Which bottle makes the biggest bubbles? Which bottle makes the smallest bubbles? Which bottle makes the most bubbles? Why?

Water Transfer

Give your child an empty ice cube tray and a spoon. Set out a bowl of water. Let your child use the spoon to transfer the water from the bowl to the compartments in the ice cube tray.

Variation: Have your child use an eyedropper or a turkey baster instead of a spoon.

Dear Parents,

We have been learning about the water in our world, including rain, lakes and oceans. When you do the following activities with your child, talk about all the different places you see water outside.

Water Search

Take your child on a walk outside to search for water. How many water puddles can he or she find? Are there any creeks or streams nearby? What about water fountains? Have your child describe the water at each place. Is the water moving or still? Is it making a noise? What color is it? Is the water dirty or clean?

Rain Song
Sung to: "Frere Jacques"

It is raining, it is raining,
On my head, on my head.
Pitter, pitter, pat, pat,
Pitter, pitter, pat, pat.
Now I'm wet, now I'm wet.

It is raining, it is raining,
On the plants, on the plants.
Pitter, pitter, pat, pat,
Pitter, pitter, pat, pat.
Now they'll grow, now they'll grow.

It is raining, it is raining,
On the dirt, on the dirt.
Pitter, pitter, pat, pat,
Pitter, pitter, pat, pat.
Now there's mud, now there's mud.

Gayle Bittinger

Mini Rain Cycle

Have your child fill a jar partway with water and screw on its lid. Use a permanent felt-tip marker to mark the level of water in the jar. Let your child place the jar in a sunny window. Observe the jar over the next few days. What is happening to the level of the water? Where is the water going? (The heat from the sun is warming up the water in the jar so that some of it is evaporating and collecting at the top of the jar.) This experiment demonstrates how the rain cycle works.

Dear Parents,

We are learning about how to care for our water and the animals that live in it. Below are some activities you and you child can do at home to learn more about water pollution and conservation.

Yucky, Yucky, Poo
Sung to: "The Bear Went Over the Mountain"

There's something polluting our water,
There's something polluting our water,
There's something polluting our water,
I'll tell you what it is.

It is a _____,
It is a _____,
It is a _____,
Yucky, yucky, poo.
    (Hold nose.)

Insert the name of something that pollutes the water in the blanks.

Jean Warren

Conserving Water

Show your child how much water we can conserve if we turn the water on and off while brushing our teeth. Place a large.measuring cup or a bowl under the faucet. Let your child brush his or her teeth while the water is running into the cup. Set the cup aside and place another large measuring cup or a bowl under the faucet. Have your child brush his or her teeth again, this time turning the water on and off as it is needed. When your child is finished, set the second cup of water by the first. Which has more in it? Which way of brushing is better for conserving water?

Water Garbage

The plastic ring-type holders found on six-packs of aluminum cans should always be disposed of in the garbage. However, sometimes they end up in the water where fish and other animals that live there get caught in them. Let your child help make these plastic holders less of a hazard. Before throwing one away, give it to your child and let him or her use scissors to cut through each ring in the holder. (This will prevent any

animal from getting stuck in it.) Then have your child throw the holder in the garbage.

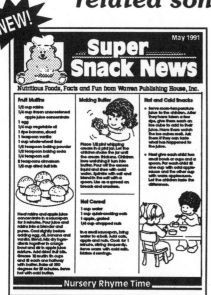

Totline Books

Super Snacks - 120 seasonal sugarless snack recipes kids love.

Teaching Tips - 300 helpful hints for working with young children.

Teaching Toys - over 100 toy and game ideas for teaching learning concepts.

Piggyback Songs - 110 original songs, sung to the tunes of childhood favorites.

More Piggyback Songs - 195 more original songs.

Piggyback Songs for Infants and Toddlers - 160 original songs, for infants and toddlers.

Piggyback Songs in Praise of God - 185 original religious songs, sung to familiar tunes.

Piggyback Songs in Praise of Jesus - 240 more original religious songs.

Holiday Piggyback Songs - over 240 original holiday songs.

Animal Piggyback Songs - over 200 original songs about animals.

1•2•3 Art - over 200 open-ended art activities.

1•2•3 Games - 70 no-lose games to ages 2 to 8.

1•2•3 Colors - over 500 Color Day activities for young children.

1•2•3 Puppets - over 50 puppets to make for working with young children.

1•2•3 Murals - over 50 murals to make with children's open-ended art.

1•2•3 Books - over 20 beginning concept books to make for working with young children.

Teeny-Tiny Folktales - 15 folktales from around the world plus flannelboard patterns.

Short-Short Stories - 18 original stories plus seasonal activities.

Mini-Mini Musicals - 10 simple musicals, sung to familiar tunes.

Small World Celebrations - 16 holidays from around the world to celebrate with young children.

Special Day Celebrations - 55 mini celebrations for holidays and special events.

Yankee Doodle Birthday Celebrations - activity ideas for celebrating birthdays of 30 famous Americans.

"Cut & Tell" Scissor Stories for Fall - 8 original stories plus patterns.

"Cut & Tell" Scissor Stories for Winter - 8 original stories plus patterns.

"Cut & Tell" Scissor Stories for Spring - 8 original stories plus patterns.

Seasonal Fun - 50 two-sided reproducible parent flyers.

Alphabet Theme-A-Saurus - the great big book of letter recognition.

Theme-A-Saurus - the great big book of mini teaching themes.

Theme-A-Saurus II - the great big book of more mini teaching themes.

Toddler Theme-A-Saurus - the great big book of toddler teaching themes.

Alphabet and Number Rhymes - reproducible take-home books.

Color, Shape & Season Rhymes - reproducible take-home books.

Object Rhymes - reproducible take-home books about seasonal objects such as hearts, pumpkins and turkeys.

Animal Rhymes - reproducible pre-reading books using repetition and rhyme about animals.

Our World - more than 120 easy environmental activities.

"Mix & Match" Animal Patterns - multi-sized patterns for 58 different animals.

"Mix & Match" Everyday Patterns - multi-sized patterns for 58 different everyday objects.

"Mix & Match" Nature Patterns - multi-sized patterns for 58 different nature objects.

ABC Space - the great big space unit with alphabet cards.

ABC Farm - the great big farm unit with alphabet cards.

ABC Zoo - the great big zoo unit with alphabet cards.

ABC Circus - the great big circus unit with alphabet cards.

Available at school supply stores and parent/teacher stores or write for our *FREE* catalog.

Warren Publishing House, Inc. • P.O. Box 2250, Dept. B • Everett, WA 98203